This Peppa Pig book belongs to
....

LADYBIRD BOOKS

UK | USA | Canada | Ireland | Australia
India | New Zealand | South Africa

Ladybird Books is part of the Penguin Random House group of companies
whose addresses can be found at global.penguinrandomhouse.com.
www.penguin.co.uk www.puffin.co.uk www.ladybird.co.uk

Penguin
Random House
UK

First published 2019
001

Adapted by Lauren Holowaty

This book is based on the TV series *Peppa Pig*.
Peppa Pig is created by Neville Astley and Mark Baker.

www.peppapig.com

Printed in China

A CIP catalogue record for this book is available from the British Library
ISBN: 978-0-241-37584-6

All correspondence to:
Ladybird Books, Penguin Random House Children's,
80 Strand, London, WC2R 0RL

Contents

Answer: Grandpa Pig, Peppa and George met five people on their way to Mummy and Daddy Pig.

Peppa's Mega Trail

Grandpa Pig is taking Peppa and George to Mummy and Daddy Pig in the garden, but they keep getting lost! Help them find their way along the right trail. Colour in everyone they meet on the way.

My Favourites

Peppa loves Teddy, jumping up and down in muddy puddles, and her best friend, Suzy Sheep. What are your favourite things? Circle your favourite thing in each bubble.

Sprinkly Sprinkles!

Peppa is helping Daddy Pig get ready for Mummy Pig's surprise party! Use your brightest colours to help her decorate all the party food. You could add some colourful sprinkles to the cake!

Story Time

The Doll Hospital

Peppa, George and Suzy Sheep are playing outside with their favourite toys, Teddy, Mr Dinosaur and Penguin.
Squelch! Squelch! Splash! Splash!
"Yippee!" cries Peppa, as they jump up and down in muddy puddles.
"This is so much fun!"

"*Squeak! Squeak!*" says Peppa in a tiny voice.
"What's that, Teddy?" asks Peppa in her normal voice.
"You want to jump in muddy puddles, too? OK!"
Peppa splashes Teddy up and down in a muddy puddle.
Then, she slips over and accidentally sits on her in the mud.
"Oops! Sorry I sat on you, Teddy!"

"Ooh, Teddy," says Mummy Pig. "You look a bit tired and muddy."
"You should take her to the Doll Hospital," says Suzy. "I took Penguin there and now he's as good as new. It's where toys go to get better."
"Mummy," says Peppa, "can we take Teddy to the Doll Hospital, please?"
"What a good idea!" says Mummy Pig.

On the way to the Doll Hospital, Suzy explains that the hospital washes the toys and fills them with stuffing. "They even give them new voices!"
Suzy presses Penguin's tummy. "You are my best friend, Suzy! I love you a lot, Suzy!" Penguin says.
"Wow!" gasps Peppa, impressed.

"Hello, Miss Rabbit," says Peppa.
"Welcome to the Doll Hospital," says Miss Rabbit, "where we turn dolls like this –" she holds up an old doll in one hand – "into dolls like this."
In her other hand is a sparkly new doll.
"Oooh!" The children gasp excitedly.

Peppa holds up Teddy to show Miss Rabbit.
"What is it?" asks Miss Rabbit. "A mouse or a dog?"
"She's a bear!" cries Peppa. "She's called Teddy."
"Teddy looks a bit floppy," says Miss Rabbit, "but nothing that some extra stuffing from the machine won't fix."
"Teddy likes being floppy, thank you, Miss Rabbit," says Peppa.

"Would Teddy like a new outfit, then?" suggests Miss Rabbit, holding up a sailor's uniform.
"Teddy doesn't want to be a sailor," says Peppa.
"How about a pilot?" asks Miss Rabbit.
"No," replies Peppa.
"Deep-sea diver? Princess?"
"No," says Peppa. "No."

"I think Teddy is happy without any clothes, thank you, Miss Rabbit," says Peppa.
"What about Mr Dinosaur, George?" says Miss Rabbit. "Would he like some clothes?"
"No!" says George. He doesn't like seeing Mr Dinosaur wearing clothes.

"I see," says Miss Rabbit. "Well, would Teddy like some new eyes, then?"
Miss Rabbit brings out a jar of different eyes for toys to show everyone.
"We've got green eyes, blue eyes or even these googly eyes!"
Miss Rabbit holds lots of different eyes up against Teddy.

Peppa looks at the new eyes. She doesn't like them at all.
"Teddy's eyes don't need changing, thank you, Miss Rabbit," she says.
"What about Mr Dinosaur . . ." begins Miss Rabbit, "does he want some new –"
"No!" cries George.

Next, Miss Rabbit plays lots of different voices that the hospital could give Teddy and Mr Dinosaur.
"That's not what Teddy sounds like," says Peppa.
"There's one last thing I can do for Teddy," says Miss Rabbit. "Give her a wash."
"No," says Peppa. "Teddy doesn't need a wash, thank you."

"I'm finished, and it's good news," says Miss Rabbit. "There's nothing wrong with Teddy or Mr Dinosaur."
"That's wonderful!" says Mummy Pig.
"So, would you like to pay with cash or a credit card?" asks Miss Rabbit.
"Oh," says Mummy Pig, handing over her card.
"I love you just the way you are, Teddy!" says Peppa. Everyone laughs.

Story Quiz

Peppa is great at remembering things. How good is your memory? What do you remember from the Doll Hospital story? Try answering these questions to find out.

1 What did Teddy get covered in? Circle the correct answer.

jelly mud ice cream

2 Circle all the toys that went to the Doll Hospital.

3 What did Teddy get from the Doll Hospital? Circle the correct answer.

a haircut a wash

a new voice nothing

Answers: 1: Teddy was covered in mud, 2: Penguin, Teddy and Mr Dinosaur went to the Doll Hospital, 3: Teddy got nothing from the Doll Hospital!

Muddy Mud Everywhere!

Squelch! Squelch! Splash! Splash! Colour in the picture to show how muddy Peppa, Suzy, George and the toys are!

Who Am I?

Oh dear! These toys are all wearing disguises and are covered in mud! Can you help Peppa, George, Suzy and Candy Cat find their own toys?

Do you know whose toy is whose? Draw lines to connect the toys with their owners.

Answers: Peppa's toy is Teddy, Candy's toy is Cat, Suzy's toy is Penguin, George's toy is Mr Dinosaur.

Odd One Out

Help Peppa and George spot the odd one out. Use a pencil to draw a circle around the thing that is different in each row.

Answers: 1: Butterfly, 2: Pumpkin, 3: Umbrella, 4: Daddy Pig's Chair.

Opposites

Big is the opposite of small, and hot is the opposite of cold. Look at all the pictures. Which sentences are correct? Draw a circle around the right ones.

Stretch your arms up in the air as high as you can. What is the opposite of up?

1

a It is a hot day.

b It is a cold day.

2

a Daddy Pig is wet.

b Daddy Pig is dry.

3

a Peppa and George are clean.

b Peppa and George are dirty.

4

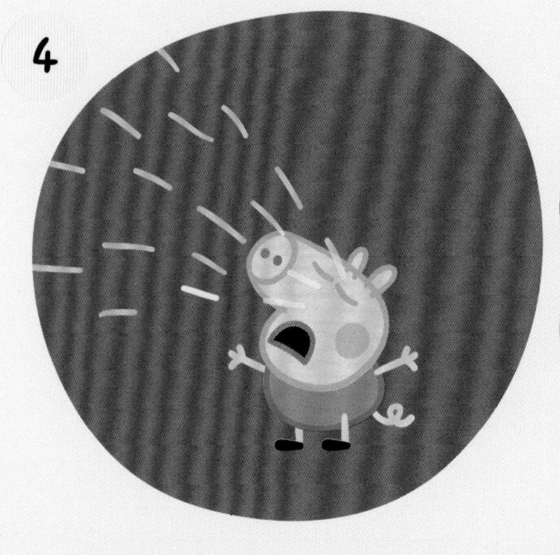

a George is sad.

b George is happy.

5

a Now George is sad.

b Now George is happy.

Answers: 1: b. It is a cold day, 2: a. Daddy Pig is wet, 3: b. Peppa and George are dirty, 4: a. George is sad, 5: b. Now George is happy.

Trip to the Zoo

Madame Gazelle has taken Peppa and her playgroup friends to the zoo. Here is a photo of them in the Butterfly House. Find all the picture pieces in the big picture and tick below each time you find one.

How many butterflies can Peppa and her friends see?

Did you know that butterflies get most of the food they need from flowers?

Answer: There are eight butterflies.

Blowing Bubbles

Peppa and George love blowing bubbles.
Everyone loves blowing bubbles! Hold a crayon in each hand, then draw lots of bubbly shapes across the page.
What different bubble shapes did you make?

Story Time

Mummy Pig's Book

Mummy Pig is working on the computer. *Tap! Tap! Tap!*
"Mummy," says Peppa, "can we play Happy Mrs Chicken on the computer?"
"Not at the moment, Peppa," replies Mummy Pig. "I just need to finish the important book I'm writing, and then you can play."

"After lots of hard work, I've finished my book," says Mummy Pig.
"Hooray!" cheers Peppa. "Now George can play Happy Mrs Chicken!"

"Forty-ninety-ten-million-hundred-and-twelve! Well done, George. That's the highest score ever!" cries Peppa.
"Oops," says Mummy Pig. "I forgot to save my work. Let me save it now. Save, close, send. Great! Now it's going to be made into a storybook!"

The next morning, Mummy Pig arrives at Peppa's playgroup with lots of copies of her new book.
"Thank you for coming to read your new book to us today, Mummy Pig," says Madame Gazelle.
"It's very exciting," says Mummy Pig. "These books are so new, I haven't even opened one yet!"

Madame Gazelle tells the children they must listen politely, as Mummy Pig has worked hard on her book. "Even if it is not very good," she adds.
"Thank you, Madame Gazelle," says Mummy Pig. "My book is about an onion."
"Oooh!" cry the children.
"*Once upon a time, there was an onion called Funny Onion*," begins Mummy Pig. Then, she turns the page. "*Four-nine-six-eight-five-nine* . . . oh!"

The rest of Mummy Pig's book is full of one big, long number!
The children flick through their books.
"This is not what I wrote!" says Mummy Pig. "What is *four-nine-six-eight-five-nine . . .*?"
"It's George's Happy Mrs Chicken high score!" cries Peppa.
"But where's my 'Funny Onion' story? It's gone!" Mummy Pig gasps.
"I'm sorry, children, but I can't read to you today."

"Oh," the children sigh sadly.
"Can you remember the story, Mummy Pig?" asks Madame Gazelle.
"Yes," says Mummy Pig.
"Then just tell us the rest," says Madame Gazelle.
"OK," says Mummy Pig, closing the book and putting it down.

"*Once upon a time, there was an onion called Funny Onion,*" begins Mummy Pig. "*It was a beautiful day, and Funny Onion was walking happily down a path alongside the mountains. All he wanted to do that day, and every other day, was make people laugh.*"
"Hee! Hee!" the children laugh.

"*Just then, a carrot came walking along. Funny Onion gave the carrot a great big smile, but the carrot immediately started crying! Funny Onion wanted to make people laugh, but he always made them cry because he was an onion.*"
"What a beautiful, sad ending," says Madame Gazelle, clapping.
"No, wait," says Mummy Pig. "It's not finished."

"Oh, I see," says Madame Gazelle. "Carry on then, Mummy Pig."
"Funny Onion continued to walk along the path. 'I will search the world to learn how to be funny,' he said. Soon after, he met a tomato who told him to wear a funny hat. But when Funny Onion wore the funny hat, everyone still cried. Even the tomato cried!"

"Next, Funny Onion met a banana who said, 'Wear some funny shoes!' So, Funny Onion put on some funny shoes. But people still cried. The banana burst into tears, too. Funny Onion was about ready to give up, when a pineapple appeared and whispered in his ear . . .
What do you think the pineapple said?" Mummy Pig asks the children.

“Wear a funny red nose!” shouts Suzy Sheep.
“Wear a purple wig!” shouts Rebecca Rabbit.
“Very good!” says Mummy Pig. “But what the pineapple really said was,
‘Do something funny!’” She went back to telling her story. “*So, Funny Onion jumped around blowing raspberries and wiggling, and everyone laughed so much they fell over. The end.*”
“Marvellous!” cries Madame Gazelle. “I think it speaks to all of us!”

The parents arrive to pick up the children.
“I’ve been to the bookshop, Mummy Pig,” says Mr Elephant. “It’s full of your books!
What did you mean by *four-five-three-nine-six-seven*?”
“Well, er, actually . . .” begins Mummy Pig.
“It’s probably post-narrative,” says Mr Wolf.
“Well done, Mummy Pig!” says Madame Gazelle.
The children love Mummy Pig’s book and the parents do, too!

Spot the Difference

Look at these two pictures of Mummy Pig reading her book at playgroup. Can you spot five differences between the two pictures?

Answers: 1: Mummy Pig is now wearing a hat, 2: A clock has appeared on the wall, 3: Peppa's book has changed colour, 4: Pedro Pony has replaced Danny Dog, 5: The pen pot has disappeared.

Rhyme Time

Peppa loves books with rhyming words in them! Which of the words below rhyme with each other? Draw lines to match them all into rhyming pairs.

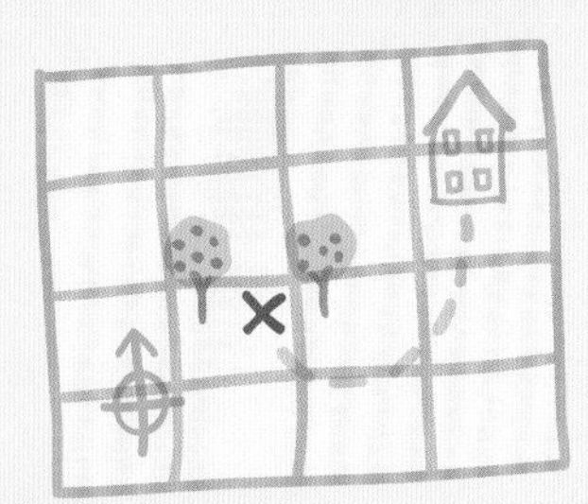

1 map

a jar

2 car

b shell

3 bat

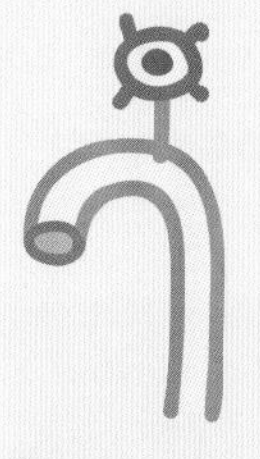

c tap

4 bell

d cat

Answers: The rhyming pairs are: 1–c, 2–a, 3–d and 4–b.

Peppa's Story Cards

Peppa and Suzy love making up their own stories, just like Mummy Pig! Ask a grown-up to carefully cut out the story cards on the following pages. Then, use the cards to make up your own stories! Shuffle all the cards, then pick four at random and try to think of a story that would link them all. Read the example below to help you.

Think of a title for each of your stories.

Example story idea:

Moon Adventure

Once upon a time, Peppa and George were packing their bags to go on an adventure! "Where should we go today, George?" asked Peppa. "Moooooon!" George cheered.

Peppa and George jumped in their rocket. *Five, four, three, two, one . . . Blast off!* They headed to the moon.

"Surprise!" said all of Peppa and George's friends when they landed. Their friends were already on the moon waiting for them!

When they'd finished exploring, Peppa and George flew back home. They were just in time to have breakfast with Mummy and Daddy Pig. "Delicious!" cried Peppa.

The end.

SP-350

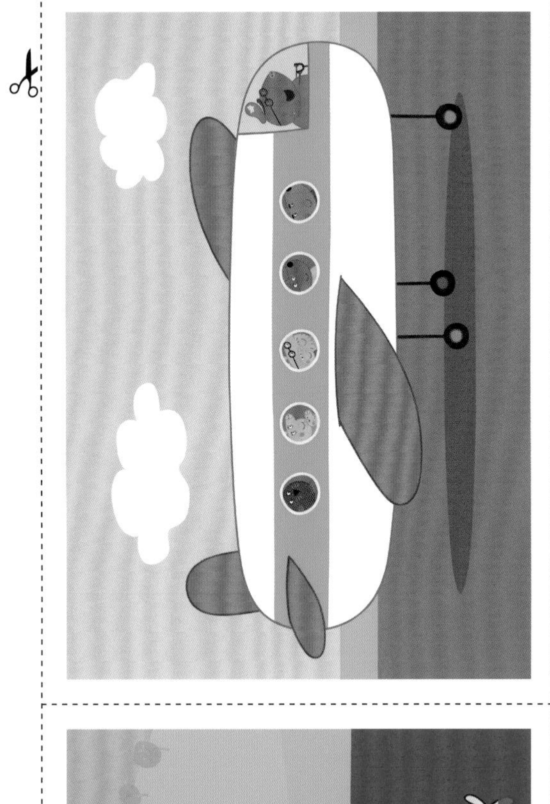

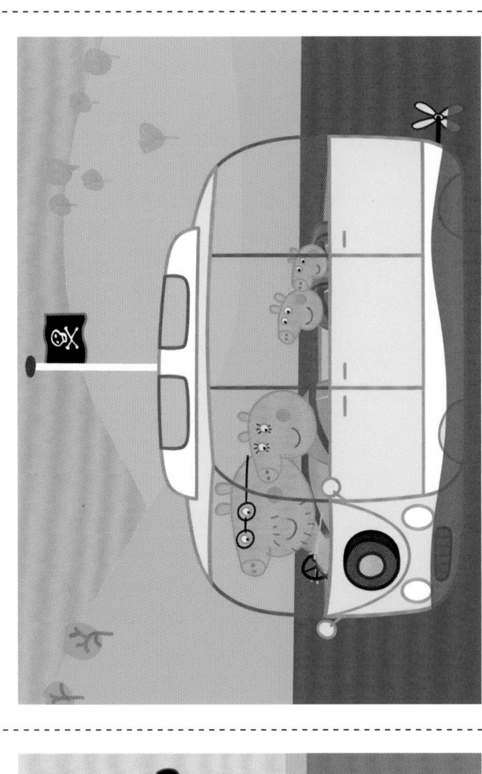

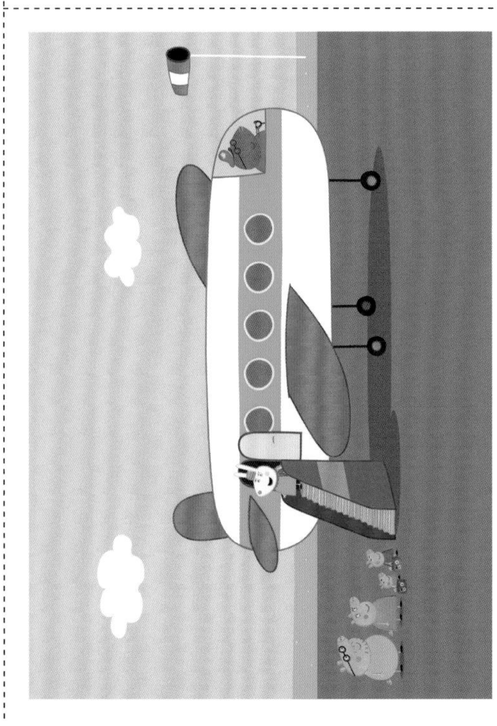

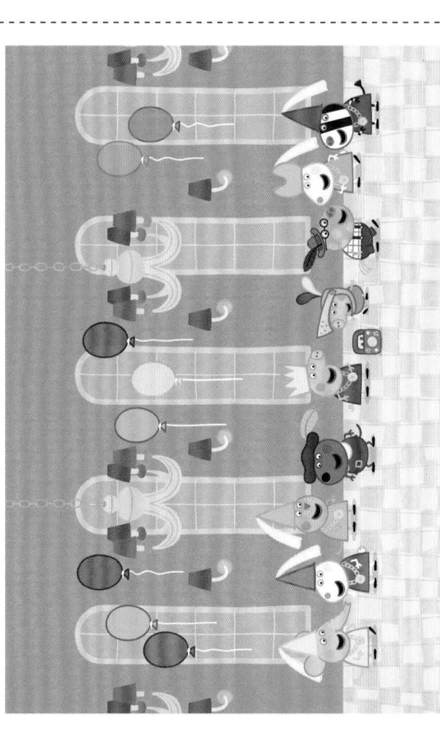

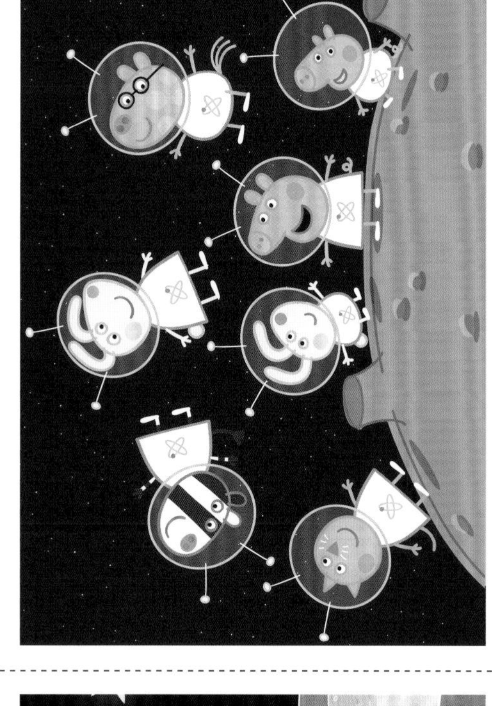
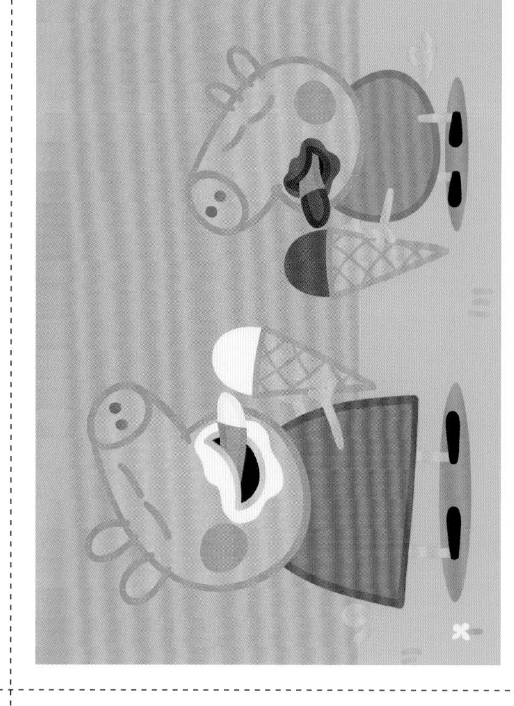

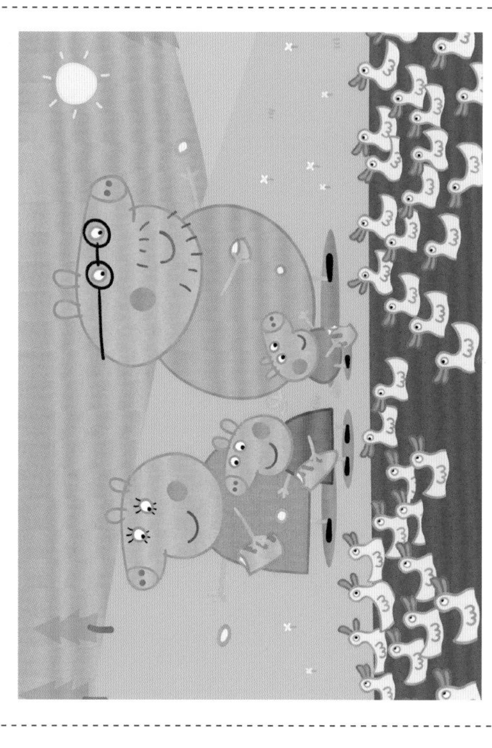

Snail Trails

Peppa and George have found a snail in Grandpa Pig's garden! Use your finger or a pencil to trace the dotted lines of the snail's trails. Slimy!

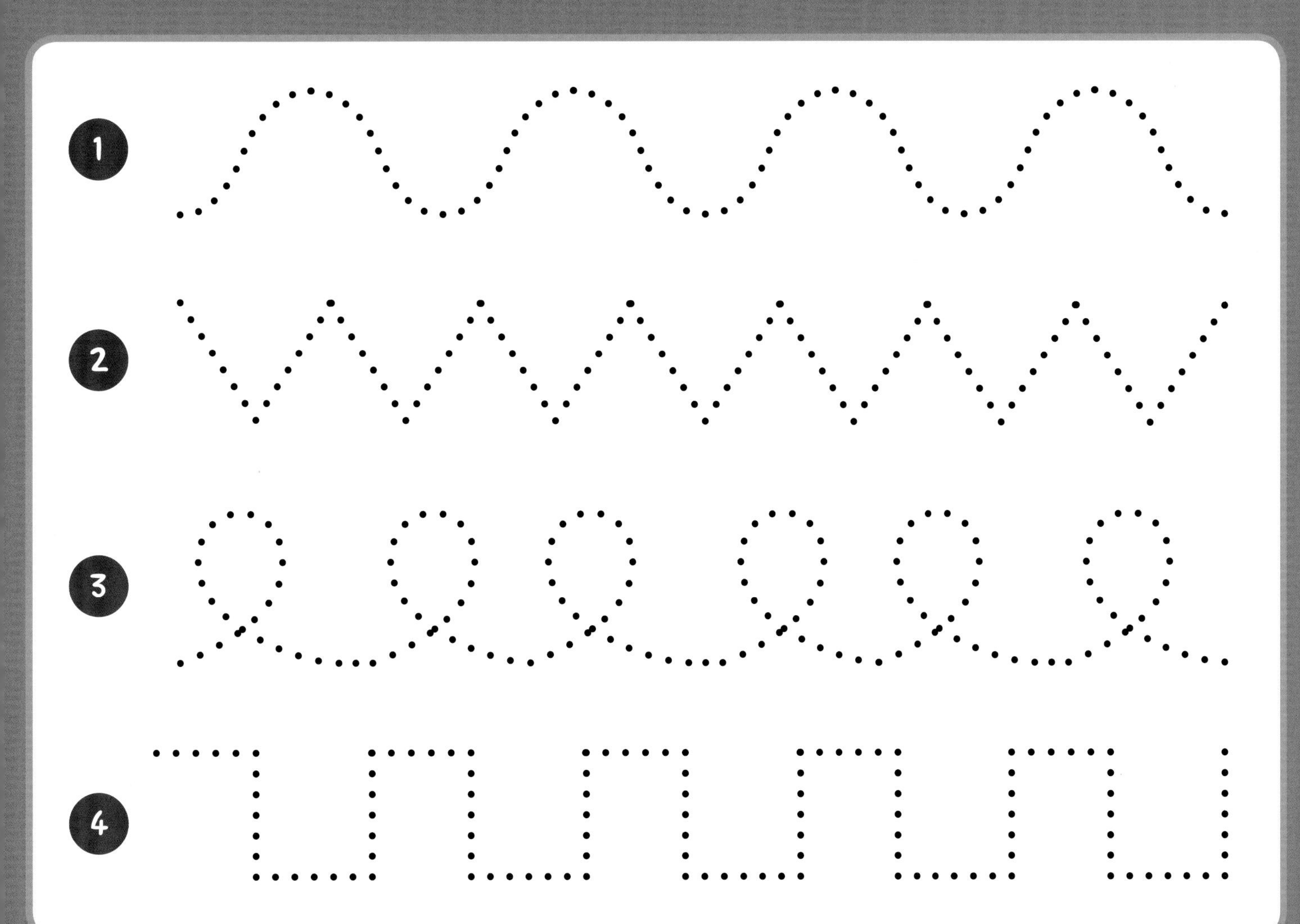

Peppa's Playgroup

Peppa's playgroup is a very colourful place. Can you find all the things at the bottom of the page in the picture? When you find them, colour them in using the right colours.

When you've finished colouring, trace the letters of each colour.

The door is
orange

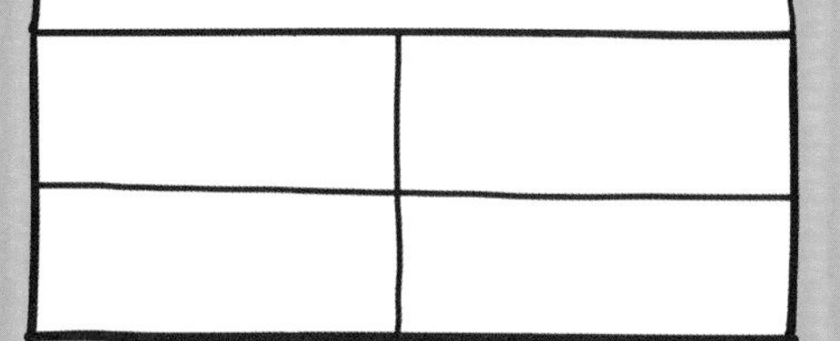

The shelves are
red

The table is
blue

Look Out, Mummy Pig!

Wheee! Mummy Pig is going so fast on her skis that she doesn't know where she's going to end up! Follow the tangled lines to find out where each leads.

Secret Surprise Birthday Card

Peppa loves surprises. Everyone loves surprises! Follow the simple steps to make this fun fold-out birthday card and surprise one of your friends.

You will need:

The page opposite

Coloured pens or pencils

Scissors

Glitter or other decorations for your card

Glue to stick your decorations on

What to do

1. Ask a grown-up to cut out the opposite page along the dotted line.

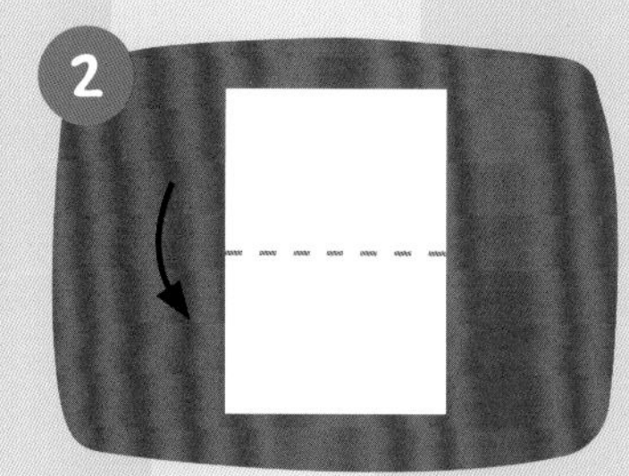

2. Fold the piece of paper in half, as shown above.

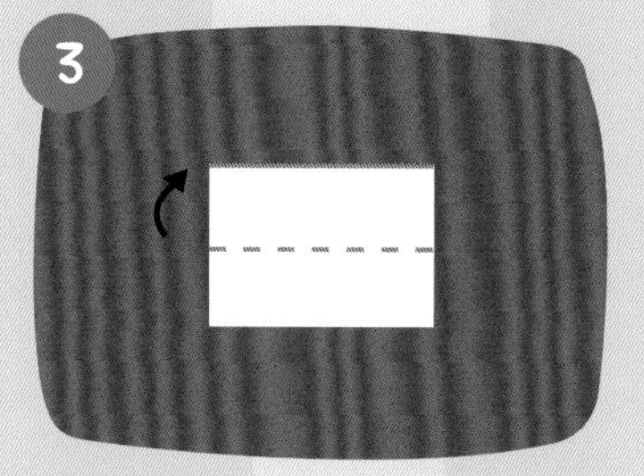

3. Fold the top half of the paper in half again, so that the top edge of the paper is in line with the middle fold.

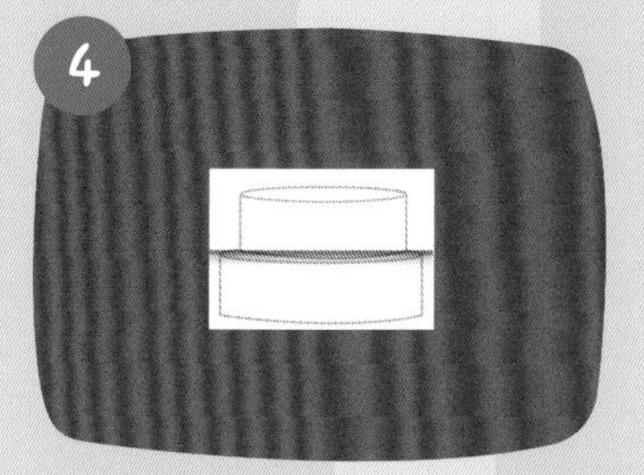

4. Next, follow the dots to draw a birthday cake on the folded paper, as shown.

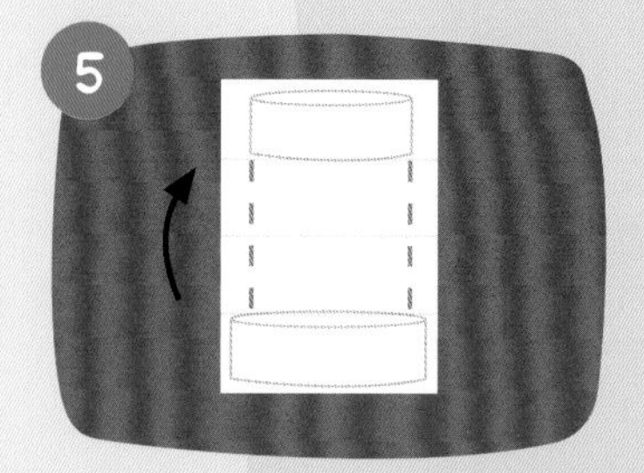

5. Once you've finished your drawing, unfold the paper. Now you will have half your cake at the top of the page and the other half of your cake at the bottom. There should be a big gap in the middle of the page.

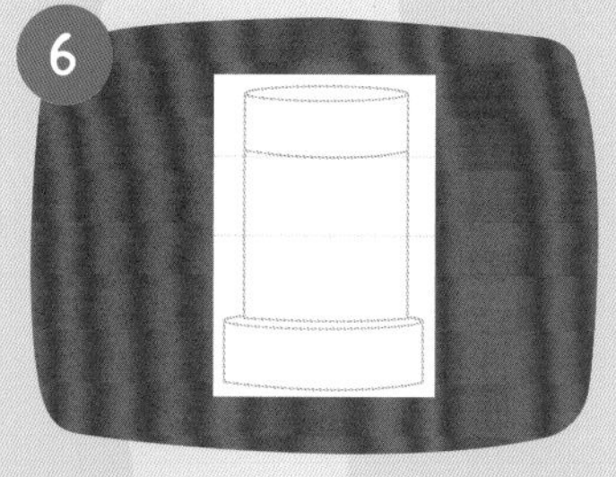

6. Connect the dots from the bottom and top halves of your cake with straight lines.

7. Write a birthday message in the middle, then colour in and decorate your cake.

8. Fold up your card and give it to your friend for their birthday. Watch them open it and find the secret surprise!

FOLD

FOLD

Colour by Numbers

It's a beautiful day and Peppa, George, Mummy and Daddy Pig have gone to the beach. Use the numbers to help you colour in the picture of them playing in the sand.

Tiny Land Adventure Game
Yikes! There's a tiny shark circling Pirate Island. Swim on three spaces to get away from it!
FINISH!
Congratulations! You made it all the way round Tiny Land. This is where your tiny adventure ends.
You stop to watch Miss Rabbit sell tiny little boat rides in the Land of Water. Miss a turn.
You will need:
· Two small objects to use as counters
· A dice
· Someone to play with

Peppa and her family are visiting Tiny Land! It's just like the real world, but very tiny. To explore Tiny Land, roll a dice and take turns with a friend moving round the board.

The winner is the first person to explore all of Tiny Land and reach the finish.

You are now in the ROAR-some Land of Dinosaurs! But the dinosaurs are tiny! Stomp on two spaces to walk with the little creatures.

Welcome to Modern Land, where it is VERY busy! Move back one space to get away from all the traffic!

START

Welcome to Tiny Land!

Congratulations, you made it to the World of Famous Places! Move on three spaces to explore lots of famous buildings.

Dinosaur Party!

Ask a grown-up to help you tear the next page out of the book, then rip it up into lots of little squares.

Stick the little squares on to the dinosaur, making it as colourful as possible.

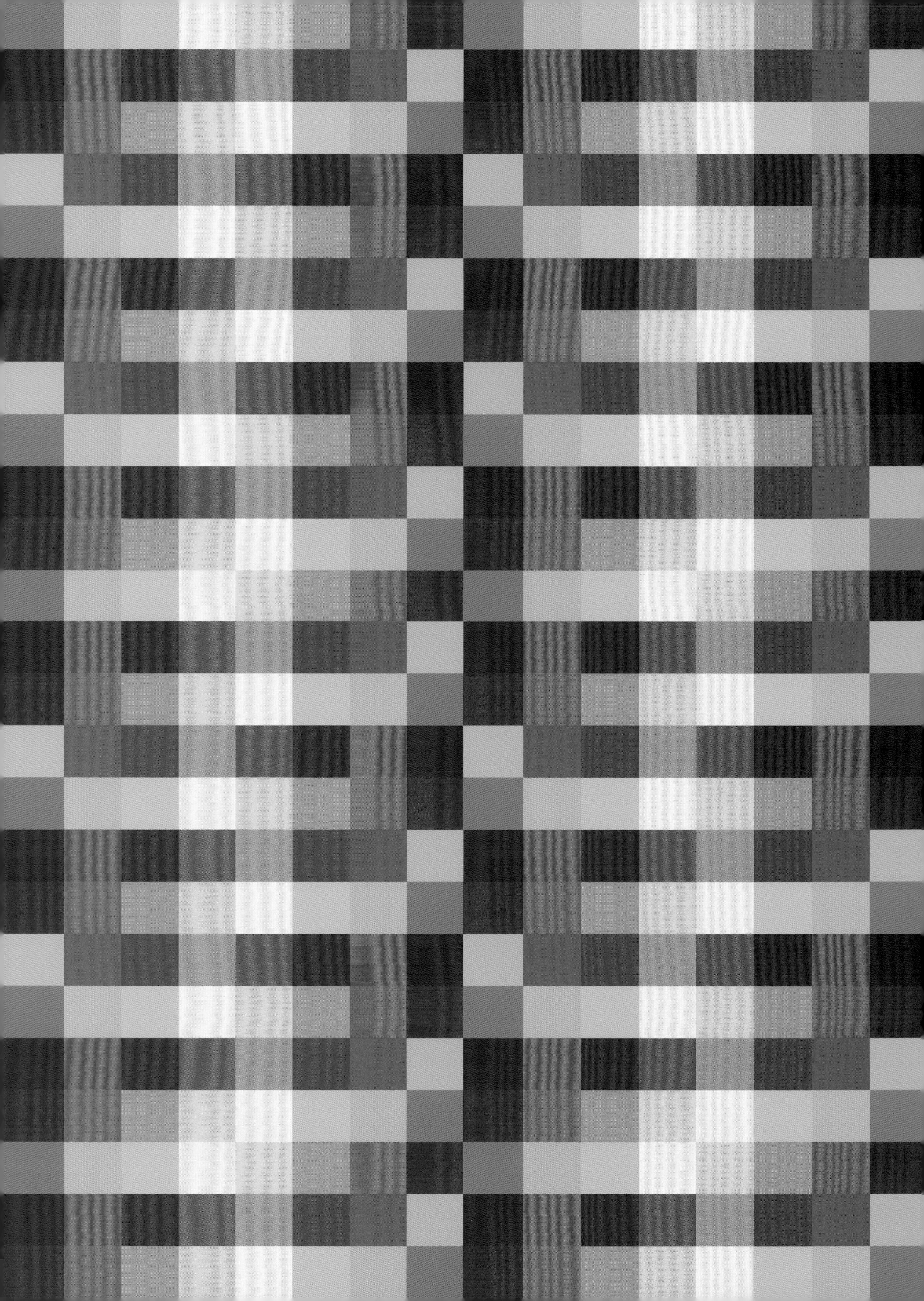

Party Pairs

George had so much fun at his dinosaur party! Can you help him tidy up? Draw lines to match the party things into pairs. Which item is the odd one out?

Answer: The spider is the odd one out.

Story Time

The Market

"Apples! Apples! Get your apples here!" shouts the fruit-seller at the market.
"Cheese! Smelly cheese!" shouts the cheese-seller.
"Fish! Nice, fresh fish!" shouts the fish-seller. Each stall sells one thing.
"Apples! Cheese! Fish! Violins! Custard! Rocket engines!" shouts Mr Fox.
He sells everything.

Peppa and her family have come to the market to do their shopping.
"Can we buy some apples, please?" Peppa asks the fruit-seller.
"What kind would you like?" asks the fruit-seller. "Big or small? Red or green?"
"We would like the apples that taste nice," says Peppa.
The fruit-seller gives Peppa an apple to try. "Mmm, lovely!" she says.
"A bag of the 'lovely' apples, please," says Mummy Pig.

"Cheese!" shouts the cheese-seller.
"Yum! Yum!" says George. He loves cheese.
"I've got a very smelly cheese here," says the cheese-seller.
"Maybe Daddy Pig should give it a sniff?" says Mummy Pig.
Sniff! Sniff! Daddy Pig sniffs the cheese. "Eugh!" he says, coughing.
"That's a strong cheese!"
Sniff! Sniff! George sniffs the cheese, too. "Yum!" he says.
He likes the smelly cheese, so they buy some.

"Can we buy some fish, please?" Peppa asks the seller at the fish stall.
"I've got trout, haddock, mackerel or squid," says the fish-seller. "Which would you like?"
"They all look good!" says Mummy Pig.
"I'll give you some of each," says the fish-seller. "Then you can make a lovely fish pie."
"Yummy!" says Peppa.

Peppa and her family walk to Mr Fox's stall.
"Bananas! Power tools! Handbags!" says Mr Fox. "I'm selling anything, really. What d'you want?"
"Nothing, thank you," says Daddy Pig. "We've bought everything we need – apples, cheese and fish."
"Oh! Why didn't you come to me first?" asks Mr Fox. "I've got all of those!"

"Do you sell apples?" Daddy Pig asks Mr Fox.
Mr Fox pulls out an apple. "You've never seen apples like these!" he says. "They're made of wood!"
"Wooden apples?" asks Peppa.
"Brilliant, aren't they?" says Mr Fox. "They'll last forever!"

“I’ve got all kinds of cheese, too,” says Mr Fox, pulling out some brightly coloured cheese slices.
“They don’t smell of much,” says Daddy Pig, sniffing them.
“That’s because they’re plastic. Guaranteed to last you a lifetime!” replies Mr Fox.
“And, it’s buy one, get four free.”
“No, thank you, Mr Fox,” says Mummy Pig.

Next, Mr Fox holds up a fish. “Look, it sings!”
He presses a button, and the fish wiggles about and starts to sing:
“*Twinkle, twinkle, little star . . .*”
“Ooh, it’s beautiful, isn’t it?” says Peppa.
“And it only needs twenty-four batteries!” adds Mr Fox.
“Can we have one, please, Daddy?” asks Peppa. “It could sing to us all day.”
“No,” replies Daddy Pig.

"Thanks, Mr Fox," says Mummy Pig. "But we really do have everything we came for."
"How about an antique china vase that will never break?" suggests Mr Fox, bouncing a vase up and down. "It's . . . er . . . made of plastic."
"It's really lovely, but we don't need anything," says Mummy Pig.
Just then, it starts to rain . . .

"Oh no, we're getting all wet!" says Peppa.
"No worries, I've got just the thing," says Mr Fox. "Umbrellas!"
"Ho! Ho! We'll take those!" says Daddy Pig, laughing.
"Yes. Four umbrellas, please," says Mummy Pig.

"It's lucky you came to my stall," says Mr Fox. "And the best thing is, just for today, buy four umbrellas . . . and you get a singing fish for free!"
"Thank you, Mr Fox," says Mummy Pig.
"*Twinkle, twinkle, little star . . .*" sings the fish.
"Oh, goody!" Peppa cheers.

Mummy and Daddy Pig burst out laughing, and so do Peppa and George.
Peppa loves the market! Everyone loves the market!

Shopping Lists

It's a very busy day at the market! Can you help everyone with their shopping? Find the things in the big picture and tick them off the shopping lists.

ball of wool
green apple
teacup
teapot
fish
tinned fruit
yellow cheese
red apple
rubber duck
vase
cake
clock
penguin
piggy bank
lamp

What Will You Buy?

What would you like to buy from the market?
Draw everything you would buy in Peppa's big shopping basket!

Which Stall?

Oh dear, some of the things from the market have gone missing! Can you find them all? Draw lines to show which stall each thing should be returned to.

Colour in each thing once you've found where it belongs.

1

a

2

b

3

c

4

d

5

e

Answers: 1–d, 2–c, 3–e, 4–b, 5–a.

Delicious Surprise!

Mummy Pig has a yummy surprise for Peppa. Join the dots to finish the picture and see what the surprise is.

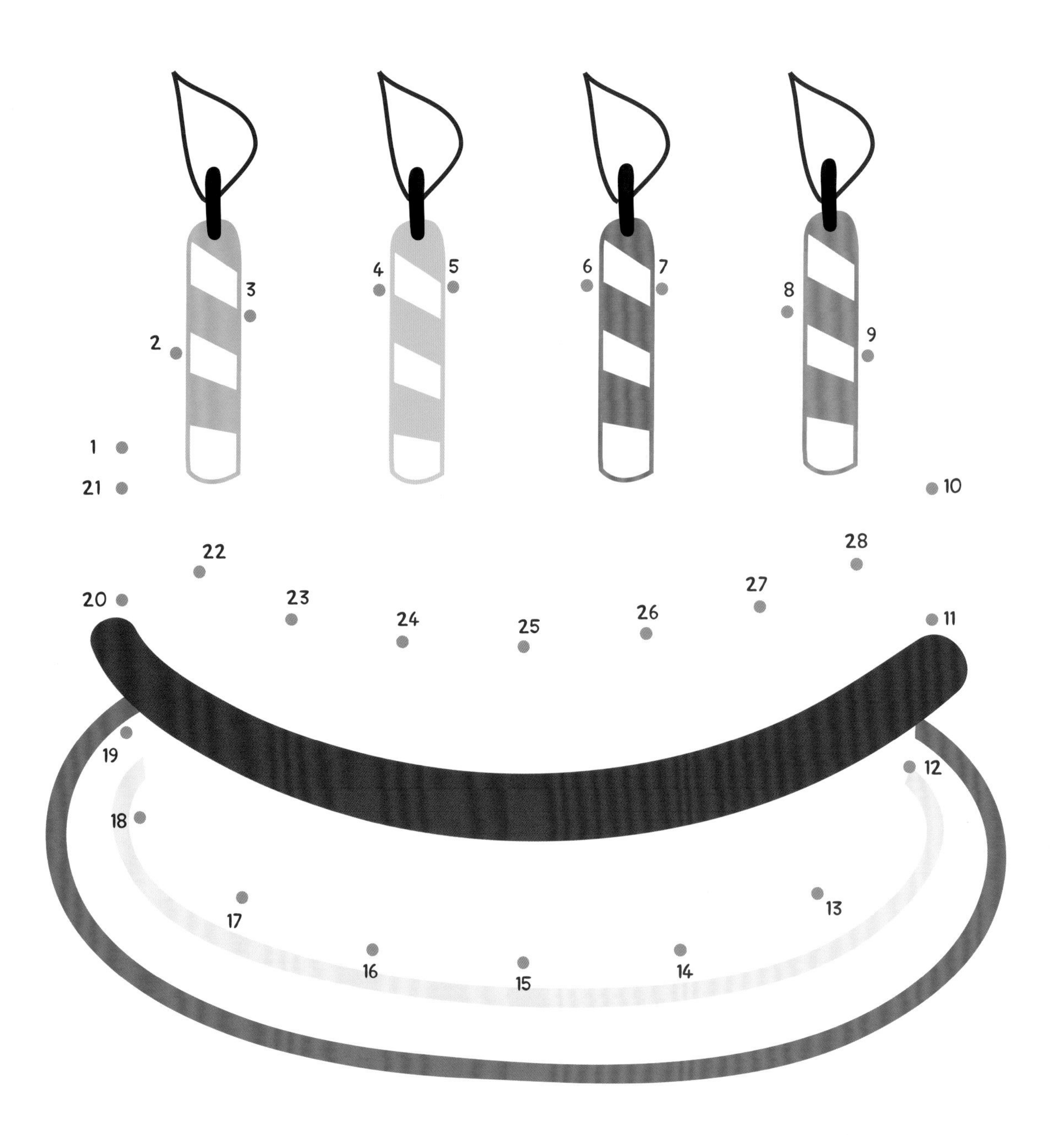

Answer: The surprise is a cake.

Dressing Up

Peppa has lots of different outfits to wear! Look at the pictures and decide what she should wear for each adventure.

Answers: 1-d, 2-a, 3-b, 4-c.

Look out for these other great Peppa Pig books!

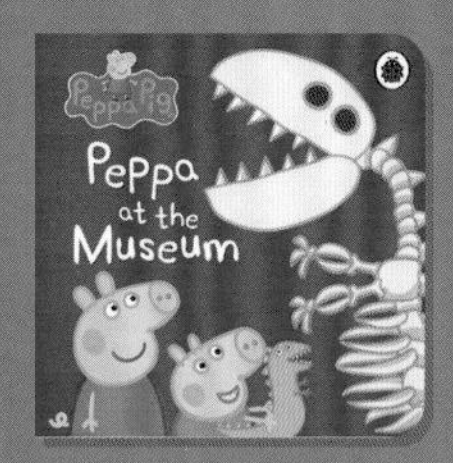